I Never Done
Nothing

Peter Leigh

Published in association with
The Basic Skills Agency

Hodder & Stoughton

Order queries: please contact Bookpoint Ltd, 39 Milton Park, Abingdon, Oxon
OX14 4TD. Telephone: (44) 01235 400414, Fax: (44) 1235 400454.
Lines are open from 9.00-6.00, Monday to Saturday, with a 24 hour message answering
service. Email address: orders@bookpoint.co.uk

British Library Cataloguing in Publication Data
A catalogue record for this title is available from The British Library

ISBN 0 340 696990

First published 1997
Impression number   10 9 8 7 6 5 4
Year   2004 2003 2002 2001 2000 1999

Typeset by Fakenham Photosetting Ltd, Fakenham, Norfolk.
Printed in Great Britain for Hodder & Stoughton Educational,
a division of Hodder Headline Plc, 338 Euston Road, London NW1 3BH
by Athenæum Press Ltd, Gateshead, Tyne & Wear.

About the play

The People

- **Raj**
- **Gary**

The Place

The school bike sheds.

What's Happening

Gary skids his bike round the corner,

and stops by his place.

Raj is already there.

He is locking his bike up.

Gary pushes his bike up into the rack.

Act 1

Gary   You going down the club tonight?

Raj   The club?

Gary   Yes.

Raj   No, I hate the club.

Gary   You were there last night!

Raj   I know! I go there, but I still hate it.

Gary   Why do you go if you hate it?

Raj   It's that Larry.

Gary   Larry?

Raj   Yeah, Larry. The one that runs it.
I hate him.

Gary   What's wrong with Larry?

Raj   I don't know! I just hate him.

Gary   Why?

Raj   I just said, I don't know!

I don't know why I hate him.

Gary   You can't just hate someone for no reason.

Raj   Well, I can. I hate Larry.

Gary   That's silly! You've got to have a reason.

Raj   No, you don't! You hate that girl, don't you?

Gary   What girl?

Raj   The one that beat you up.
That Mandy.

Gary   She didn't beat me up.
No girl ever beat me up.

Raj   Yes she did. You wanted a lick of her ice-cream, and she wouldn't give you one.

Gary   So?

Raj   And you kept going on at her, and

hanging round her, and pestering
her, and in the end she got fed up,
and stuffed the ice-cream
in your face.

Gary   So?

Raj   She held you down, and wiped the
ice-cream all round your face.

Gary   So?

Raj   And then got her friends to come
and lick it off.

Gary   Yes, but she still didn't beat me up.

Raj   Well, her.

Gary   What about her?

Raj   Well you hate her don't you?
And you've got no reason.
Well it's just the same with Larry.
I hate him. That's all.
I always have done.

(Pause)

Ever since he threw me out.

Gary He threw you out?

Raj Yes, he was great until then.

And then one night,

last night in fact,

he just threw me out.

Just like that. For no reason.

Gary For no reason?

Raj Well, there was this little rip on the

pool table. A little tiny rip!

It was only a few centimetres long.

Well perhaps a bit more.

In fact it was more like half a metre.

But it wasn't my fault.

I didn't even do it!

It was Jon-Paul.

Gary	Jon-Paul?
Raj	Yes! The big show off!
	He was showing off to everybody
	about how he could do this trick
	with the cue ball.
	Make it jump in the air.
Gary	Jump in the air?
Raj	Yes! The big show off!
Gary	And what were you doing?
Raj	I was standing behind him with the
	other cue.
Gary	What happened?
Raj	Well, he bent over the table to make
	his shot.
Gary	Yes?
Raj	Well, as he made his shot to make
	the cue ball jump in the air,
	I made my shot.

Gary And?

Raj I made him jump in the air!

Gary You mean you stuck your cue up his . . . ?

Raj Yes!

Gary What happened?

Raj He jerked up, and ripped the cloth on the pool table.

Gary So Jon-Paul ripped it!

Raj   Yes! If he hadn't have jerked,

he would never have ripped it.

But Larry blamed me.

As if it was my fault.

And then he threw me out.

For no reason.

Gary   Just for that? For a little nick on

the pool table? He threw you out?

Raj   Yes. Just for that!

*Gary finishes locking his bike, and
starts to pack his bag.
Raj slings his bag over his shoulder.*

Raj   Mind you, there was the cue!

Gary   The cue?

Raj   When Jon-Paul ripped the cloth,

everybody was laughing at him.

And he got really mad.

I don't know why.

It was only a joke.

But he threw a real wobbler.

And I only gave him a little prod.

Gary   He always did have a bad temper,
that Jon-Paul.

Raj   Exactly!

Well, he gets all mad, and then he
has a go at me.

Gary   No?

Raj   Yes! For no reason at all!

He gets his pool cue, and swipes it
at me.

Gary   Did he hit you?

Raj   No. I ducked.

He hit the wall instead.

Gary And the cue . . . ?

Raj Broke!

Gary So, just for that,

Larry threw you out?

Raj Just for that!

Just because Jon-Paul lost his

temper, and ripped

his precious pool table,

and broke his precious cue,

he threw me out.

Gary It's not fair!

Raj I know! It wasn't my fault.

They brood in silence.

Raj *(after a while)*

Mind you, there were the cups.

Gary The cups?

Raj   Yes. And the saucers . . . and the
coffee . . . and the tea . . . and the
milk and the sugar.

Gary   The saucers, the coffee, the tea, and
the milk and the sugar?

Raj   Yes . . . and the carpet!

Gary   The carpet?

Raj   Yes, but that was Jon-Paul's fault
as well.
If he hadn't have got out of the way,
everything would have been all
right.

Gary   He got out of the way?

Raj   Well after Jon-Paul had a go at me
with the snooker cue,
I got a bit angry.

Gary   Well, anyone would.
Being attacked like that.

Raj Of course they would.

Stands to reason.

Well I got a bit angry, and threw
my cue at him.

Gary Did it hit him?

Raj No, he ducked as well.

Gary What happened to the cue?

Raj Well, you know that little snack bar
that's in the club?

Gary The one where they put the cups
and the saucers?

Raj Yes, that one.

Gary And the coffee, and the tea, and the
milk and the sugar?

Raj Yes. Well, Jon-Paul was standing in
front of that.

Gary And . . . ?

Raj Well, when the cue missed

Jon-Paul, it hit that!

Gary And the cups and the saucers and
the milk and the sugar and the
coffee and the tea . . .

Raj . . . were all knocked off . . .

Gary . . . onto the carpet!

Raj Right!

Gary I see!

Raj And so Larry blames me!

As if it's my fault!

As if I wanted to break all those
cups and saucers and things.

I couldn't help it.

It was Jon-Paul, ducking out of the
way like that.

If it's anyone's fault, it's his.

But Larry blamed me. He's always
picking on me. And he threw me out.

So that's why I hate him.

And that's why I'm not going to the club.

Gary   Oh. I see.

Raj *(brightening up)*

But we could go to the centre.

Gary   The centre?

Raj   Yes! Let's go there instead.

Gary   I can't go to the centre.

Raj   Why not?

Gary   I got thrown out last night.

For no reason at all.

Just because of a silly little bin.

I ask you . . .

But the bell rings, and they go into school.

Act 2

The end of lunchtime.

Raj *is in the bike sheds, checking
his bike.*

Gary *comes running up.*

He looks excited.

Gary You know that Jon-Paul?

Raj What about him?

Gary I've just seen him, and he says he's
going to get you.

Raj He's going to get me?

Gary He says he's going to get you for
showing him up at the club.

He says he's going to stuff your
teeth so far down your throat,

you'll be eating your own breakfast.

Raj   He said that?

Gary   He said that after he's finished
you'll need a passport so people can
recognise you.

Raj   Will I?

Gary   And he gave me 10p to start the
collection for your funeral.

Raj *(looking a little pale)*

Do you think he was joking?

Gary   Joking?

No, I don't think he was joking.

Raj *(throwing his chest out)*

Well, I'd like to see him try,
that's all.

Gary   He is big.

Raj   Size doesn't matter.

Gary   And strong.

Raj Strength isn't everything.

Gary And he does do karate, and kung-fu, and he is a black belt at judo.

Raj Look, none of them things matter. In a fight there's only one thing that matters.

Gary And what's that then?

Raj Brains. You've got to have them up here.

Raj taps the side of his head.

Gary That's you finished then!

Raj Look, you don't have to worry about me. I can look after myself. I'll be ready, any time he comes.

Gary That's good because he's coming after school.

Raj   After school?

Gary   Yes. Behind the bike sheds.

I said you'd be there.

Raj   Oh, thanks!

Gary   Well, what are friends for?

I said you'd be ready for him.

I said you'd always hated him.

I said you thought he was a big prat.

I said you couldn't wait

to do him over.

I said you were going to break his

arms, and his legs.

I said you were going to shove his

face where his bum should be.

Raj   You said all that?

Gary   Yes. And that you were going to

tie him up in his own black belt.

And stuff him in the bin where he belonged.

Raj   Thanks a lot!

Gary   That's all right. Anything to help.

Raj   Look, you know you said he'd be coming after school.

Gary   Yes?

Raj   Well I just remembered.

I've got a detention after school.

Gary	A detention?
Raj	Old Smithy gave me a detention.
Gary	You've had lots of detentions.
Raj	I know.
Gary	And you've never been to one of them.
Raj	Well, that's why I've got to go to this one.
	Otherwise I'll be in real trouble!
Gary	Well that's all right.
	The detention will only last ten minutes.
	We'll wait till you've finished.
Raj	Oh no!
	This one's going on for hours and hours, because I've missed all the others.
	I won't get out until five o'clock . . .

Six o'clock . . . In fact it probably

won't be until seven

that I get out.

Gary   You're not trying to chicken out of

this, are you?

Raj   What, me? *(**Raj** sounds shocked)*

Course not! You know me.

I'm not scared of anything.

No, it's just that if I don't do this

detention I'll get expelled.

Gary   Well, what about tomorrow?

Raj   I'm going out with my Mum.

Gary   The day after?

Raj   I'm going out with my Dad.

Gary   The day after that?

Raj   I'm going out with my cousin.

Gary   But I've told Jon-Paul you'll be

waiting for him.

Raj   Well, you'll just have tell him I'm
           sorry.

           It's not that I don't want to.

           I'm dead keen.

           I want to get in there,

           and bash his brains out,

           and do him over, but I just can't

           manage it this week,

           and probably not next week neither.

Gary   Why can't you tell him yourself?

Raj   Well, I would do, but I can't.

           I'm nipping off home early before he

           sees me.

           *Raj jumps on his bike, and pedals
           off.*

Act 3

After school in the bike sheds.

Raj *is still there.*

Gary *comes in, and is surprised to see him.*

Gary Hey! I thought you were going home.

Raj I was, but then I got caught at the gates, and sent back.

Gary Well, you better get a move on now, because Jon-Paul will be here soon.

Raj That doesn't worry me.

Gary What? Even though he said he'll kill you, and stuff your teeth down your throat?

Raj   No!

Gary   Even though he's bigger than you

and stronger than you

and does karate and kung-fu

and has got a black belt in judo?

Raj   No!

Gary   You're not scared at all?

Not even one tiny little bit?

Raj   No! Not even one tiny little bit!

And I'll tell you why. Because it's

not me that needs to be scared.

It's a so-called friend of mine that

needs to be scared.

Gary   What do you mean?

Raj   Well, I saw Jon-Paul just now in the

boys' toilets.

And he said he wasn't mad at me at

all after last night.

He thought it was a great laugh.

All those coffee-cups and milk

going everywhere.

At least he wasn't mad until he met

this friend of mine.

Gary *(nervously)*

A friend of yours?

Raj　　That's what I said.

Well, this friend started stirring,
and getting Jon-Paul riled.
He kept saying that I was going
round saying what a prat Jon-Paul
was, and how I was going to smash
his face in. And how I was looking
for him, and how big I was,
and how strong I was, and how I did
karate and kung-fu and had a black
belt in judo.

Gary Oh!

Raj Which friend of mine would say
something like that do you think?

Gary I've no idea!

Raj Nor have I! Well anyway, after me
and Jon-Paul had talked for a bit,
and found out that we weren't mad
at each other.

We decided that this so-called friend
needed teaching a lesson.

Gary *(shakily)*

A lesson?

Raj   Yes! A good, hard lesson!

For stirring things up.

So we decided we'd meet here after
school, find out who it was, and do
him over good and proper.

Gary   Oh!

Raj   In fact Jon-Paul should be along
any minute now.

Gary *(fumbling with his bike)*

Well I think I better be off now.

Raj   Don't you want to see the fight.

Gary   No, I can't stop.

He pulls his bike out of the rack.

Raj   Don't you want to find out who this so-called friend is?

Gary   No . . . really! I've got to go!

I've . . . er . . . I've . . .

Raj   I think I can hear Jon-Paul now.

Gary   Bye!

Gary rides off.

He doesn't do any skids or jumps.

He just pedals very fast.